Complete the Picture

Word Problems and Picture Completion
Book 1

Created By
Judy Wilson Goddard

Graphic Design By
Danielle West
Anna Chaffin

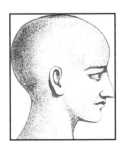

© 2008
THE CRITICAL THINKING CO.™
Phone: 800-458-4849 Fax: 831-393-3277
www.CriticalThinking.com
P.O. Box 1610 • Seaside • CA 93955-1610
ISBN 978-1-60144-169-0

Printed in the United States of America

Table of Contents

ABOUT THE AUTHOR

JUDY WILSON GODDARD has worn many hats. She served as a teacher and administrator in both private and public school settings, working with pre-school through college-level students. Throughout her diverse career, she always maintained that critical thinking was important for all levels. Since her retirement, she has continued to promote critical thinking skills by writing books for children. She is the author of many books that apply critical thinking skills to a wide range of academic disciplines. She holds three degrees in education from Georgia State University: Bachelor, Master, and Specialist.

This book is dedicated to my daughters, Joy and Janet, who are critical thinkers; and to my six grandchildren, with the hope that they too will be critical thinkers and that their apples won't always have to be red!

INTRODUCTION

Complete the Picture Math will help students think critically and review, reinforce, and apply basic math concepts. The materials require problem-solving skills and provide practice in using the strategies. Additionally, they develop comprehension, deductive reasoning, visual tracking, and fine motor skills. Students will discover that calculation and computers are useful for computation, but critical thinking skills are needed to solve problems.

In addition to critical thinking and math skills, other curriculum areas are incorporated: science, language arts, and art. Students are naturally curious about animals; therefore, the materials include animal facts, (thus incorporating science). Language arts skills are strengthened as students read and determine the relevant as well as the irrelevant phrases, statements, and information needed for solving the problems. Picture completion provides a challenge for art and creating. These curriculum areas are combined and taught in a way that is fun, challenging, and rewarding to students.

Math puzzles and problems are everywhere. When students feel the thrill of discovering, creating, and exploring the shapes, patterns, and relationships of the real world, they will grow to love and apply math skills. Math strategies and skills include guess and check, draw a picture, make a list, look for a pattern, break the problem down into simpler pieces, work backward, and use logical reasoning.

These strategies will be useful in school and everyday life. The earlier these skills are learned, practiced, and applied, the more they help students to think critically and apply math problem solving in their everyday life. Hopefully, this will enable students to use critical thinking skills without even thinking about them. This combination will build self-confidence and improve self-esteem, something that educators should work to instill in every student.

Nov 30/21

Animals

There are 20 animals all on the farm.
Some turkeys are eating grain.
Some chickens are eating grain.
Some ducks are eating grain.
How many animals are on the farm? _____

Complete and color the picture.

Alligator

Tony likes to walk to the pond to see the alligators.
It is 2 miles from Tony's house to the pond.
How many miles is it from the pond to Tony's house? _____

Complete and color the picture.

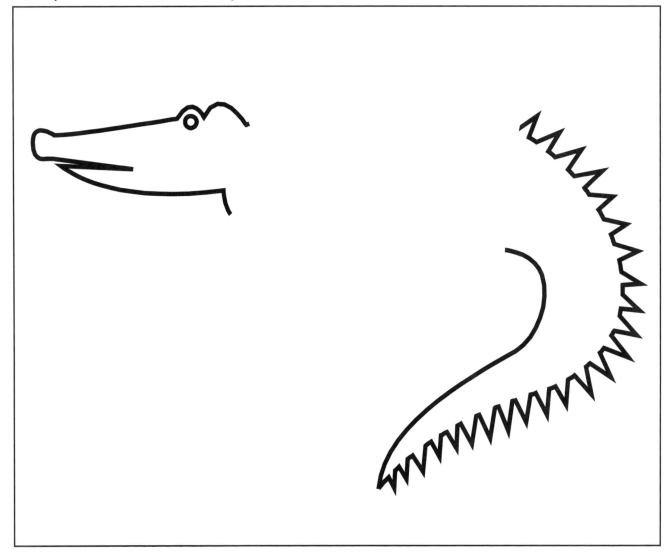

Anteater

The anteater is 4 years old.
The crocodile is twice as old.

How old is the crocodile? _____

Next year the anteater will be 5 years old.

How old will the crocodile be? _____

Next year, will the crocodile still be twice as old as the anteater? _____

Complete and color the picture.

Ape

Paul wants to go to the zoo to see the apes.
He needs 25 cents for the bus.
He has 1 dime and 3 nickels.
Does he have enough money? _____

Complete and color the picture.

Armadillo

The armadillo turned seven on October 7.

How old will he be on October 8? _____

How old was he on October 6? _____

Complete and color the picture.

5

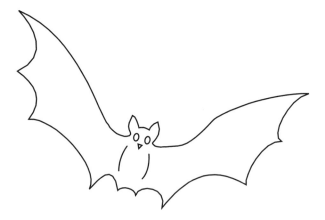

Bat

The bat flies 10 miles to the river.

Then he flies back to the barn the same way.

How many miles does the bat fly in all? _____

Complete and color the picture.

Brown Bear

The mother bear and the father bear each caught three fish.
The mother bear lost all of her fish.
How many fish does the father bear have? _____

Complete and color the picture.

Koala

There were two coconuts in a tree.
One fell and missed the big koala by 3 inches.
Another fell and missed the little koala by 10 inches.

Who was hit by more coconuts? _____

Complete and color the picture.

Panda Bear

There were eight apples in a tree.
Three fell and hit the big panda bear in the head.
Then two fell and missed the little panda bear by a few inches.

How many apples fell? _____

How many are still in the tree? _____

Complete and color the picture.

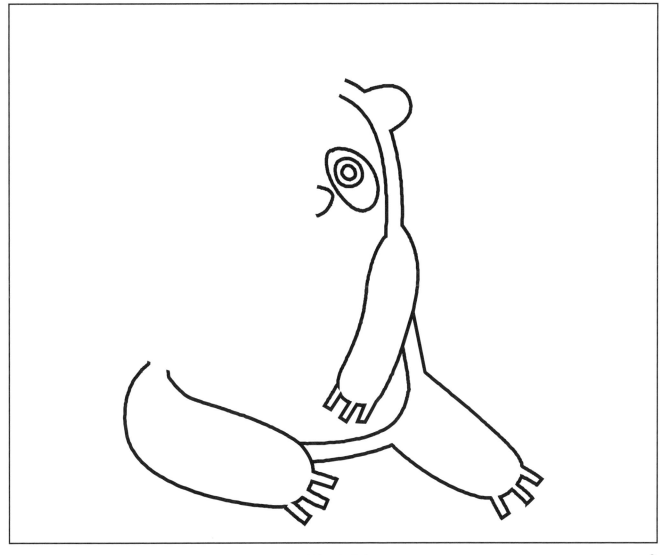

Buzzard

There were 10 children in line at the zoo.
They want to see the buzzards.
Mary is last.
How many children are in front of her? _____

Complete and color the picture.

Crane

Andy and Paul want to buy food for the crane.
At the zoo, the food costs 12 cents.
Andy has 2 pennies.
Paul has 2 nickels.
Do they have enough money? _____

Complete and color the picture.

Peacock

Andy feeds the peacocks Monday through Friday.
His dad feeds them on the weekend.
Andy wakes up and gets ready to feed the peacocks.
"Let's see," says Andy. "Yesterday was Friday and I fed the peacocks."

Should Andy get ready to feed the peacocks? _____

Why or why not?_____

_____

Complete and color the picture.

Penguin

The penguin has three friends that were all born at the same time he was.
The penguin is 8 years old.

How old are his friends? _____

Complete and color the picture.

Hawk

Amy has two coins.
One coin is a dime.
She does not have any pennies.
She wants to buy food for the hawk.
At the zoo, hawk food costs 15 cents.

Can she buy food for the hawk? _____

Why or why not?_____

_____

Complete and color the picture.

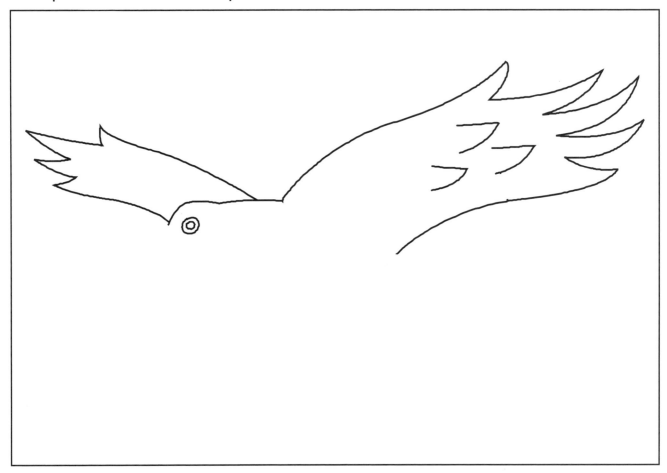

Hummingbird

The hummingbird leaves the flower garden to fly to the river.
It takes 15 minutes to fly there.
The hummingbird flies for 10 minutes.
Then he rests for 5 minutes.
How much time has passed since the hummingbird left the garden?

_____

Is he at the river yet? _____
How much longer will it take him to fly to the river if he doesn't rest

any more? _____

Complete and color the picture.

Blue Bird

The food machine at the zoo has a sign that says, "Please use correct change."
Aaron wants to buy 30 cents worth of bird food.
He has 2 quarters and one nickel.

What should Aaron do?_____

_____

Complete and color the picture.

Red Bird

Kevin put some berries in a bag.
He put 10 in each bag.
How many bags will he need if he wants to give the birds 30 berries?

_____

Complete and color the picture.

Dove

The dove had some berries.
He ate seven of them.
"I have 9 berries left," he said.
How many berries did the dove have to begin with?_____

Complete and color the picture.

Sparrow

The mother bird has two berries.
The father bird has four berries.
The baby bird has fewer berries than the father bird but more than the mother bird.
How many berries does the baby bird have? _____

Complete and color the picture.

Buffalo

Two buffalo were fed a bale of hay.
The father buffalo ate some.
The mother buffalo ate the same amount as the father buffalo.
There is not any hay left.
Can you tell if they each ate half of the hay? _____

Complete and color the picture.

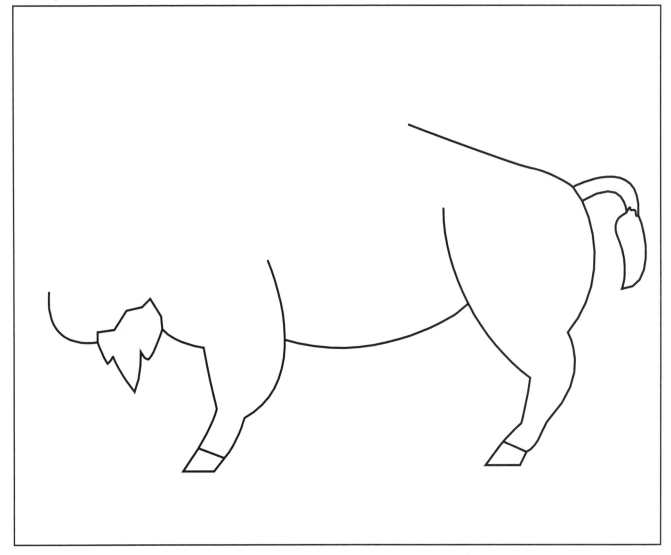

Water Buffalo

Ken has 37 apples for the water buffalo.
The bucket can only hold 36 apples.
If Ken fills the bucket, how many apples will he have left over?

Complete and color the picture.

Siamese Cat

Ruthie has some brown cats and some black cats.
She has six cats in all.
Can you tell how many brown cats she has? _____
She has the same number of brown cats as black cats.

Now can you tell how many brown cats she has? _____

Complete and color the picture.

Tabby Cat

Tommy and his cat Fluffy walked to the barn.
Do Tommy and fluffy have the same number of feet? _____

How many feet walked to the barn? _____

Complete and color the picture.

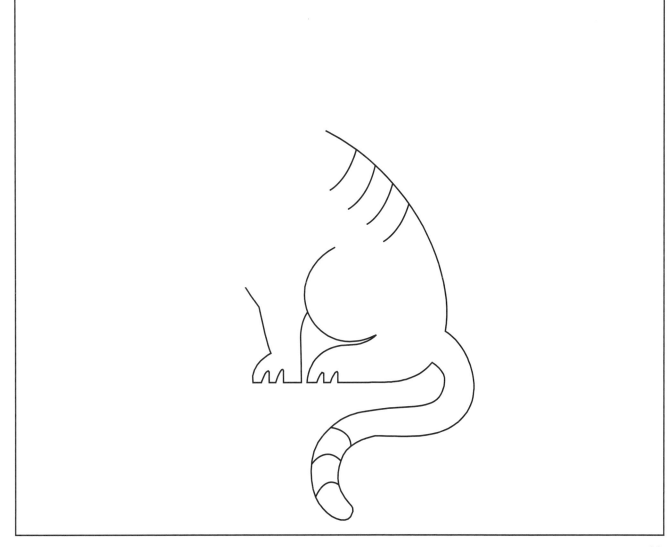

Caterpillar

Grant and Garrett went to the park.
On their way to the park, they found two caterpillars.
At the park, they found five caterpillars.
On their way home, they found two caterpillars.

How many caterpillars did they find? _____

Complete and color the picture.

Chicken

The chicken lays an egg every day.
How many eggs did she lay last week? _____

How many eggs will she lay next week? _____

How many eggs will she lay today? _____

Complete and color the picture.

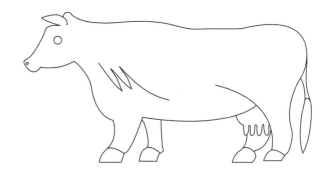

Cow

Paul began milking the cow at 3:00.
He finished at 4:00.
How long did it take him to milk the cow? _____

Complete and color the picture.

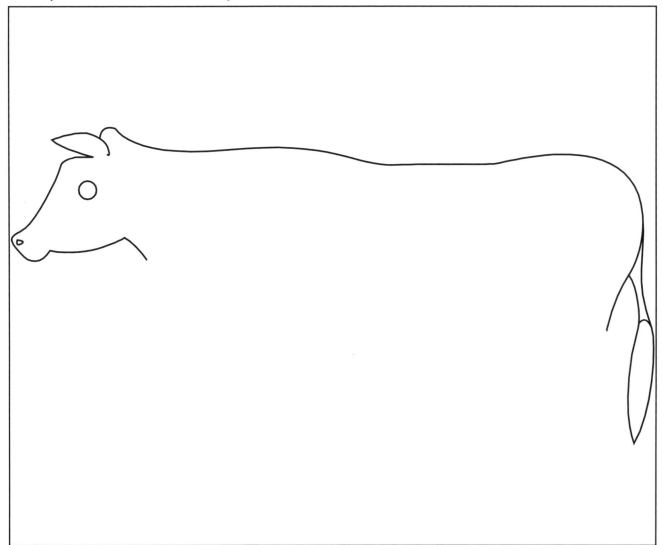

Crocodile

A big crocodile walked 3 miles to the pond.
Then he met a little crocodile, and they both walked 4 miles to another pond.
How far did the big crocodile walk? _____

Complete and color the picture.

Deer

A big deer and a little deer ate heads of lettuce.
The big deer ate six heads, while the little deer ate three heads.
Did the big deer eat an odd or even number of lettuce heads?

_____

Did the little deer eat an odd or even number of lettuce heads? _____

Complete and color the picture.

Hound

All together, two dogs have six bones.
They each eat the same number of bones.

Can you tell how many bones are left? _____

Explain your thinking to your teacher.

Complete and color the picture.

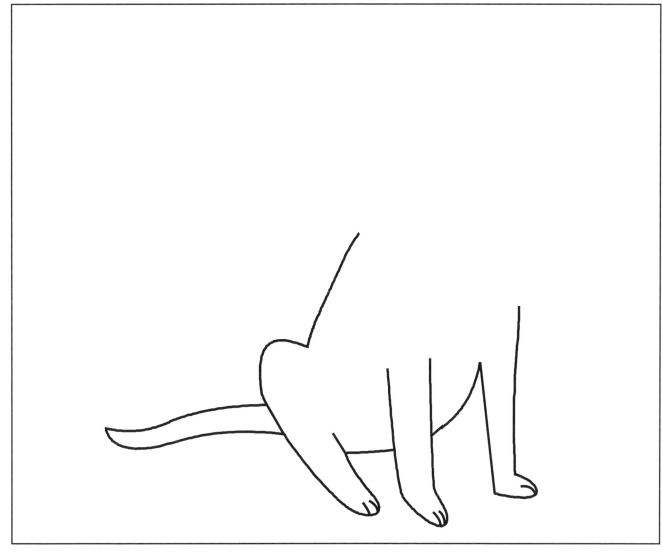

Retriever

There were three bones.
A big dog and a little dog ate them.
The big dog ate most of them.
How many did the little dog eat? _____

Complete and color the picture.

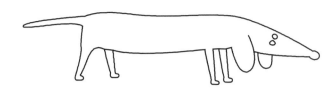

Dachshund

There were six dogs in the backyard.
Then they all left.
How many dogs are in the backyard now? _____

Complete and color the picture.

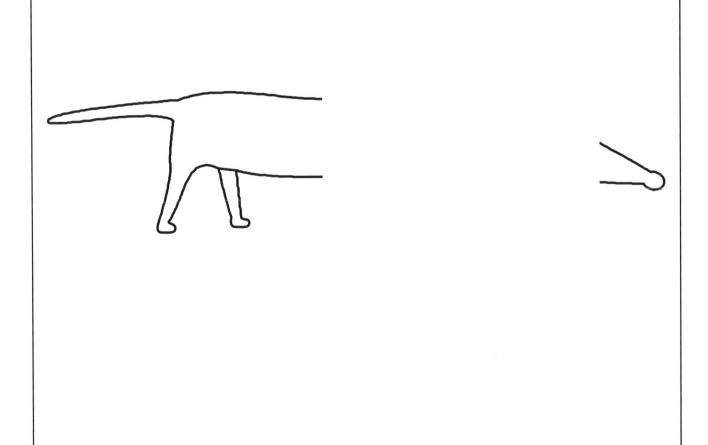

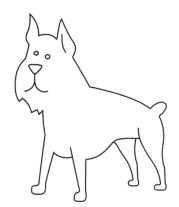

Bulldog

Jesse's family has two dogs, Spot and Blackie.
Blackie is six.
Spot is twice Blackie's age.
How old will Blackie be next year? _____

How old will Spot be next year? _____

Complete and color the picture.

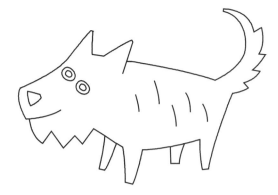

Scottie

The dog has 10 bones.
He has already eaten four.
How many bones did he have to begin with? _____

Complete and color the picture.

Donkey

One of Josh's donkeys is black.
The other is gray and black.
How many donkeys does Josh have? _____

Complete and color the picture.

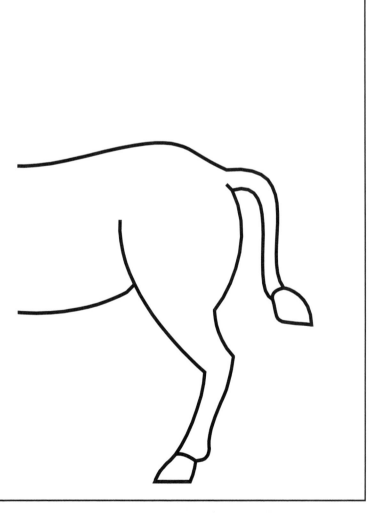

Duck

The duck walked 5 miles to the river.
When she got there, she remembered she had forgotten her baby.
She started to walk back home.
She walked 3 miles when she met another duck.

How far was she from home? _____

When the duck reaches home, how far will she have walked in all?

_____

Complete and color the picture.

Elephant

Mark went to the zoo.
He had 2 dimes and a nickel.
He lost one coin.
Does he have enough money to buy a 15 cent food snack for the

elephant? _____

How do you know? _____

_____

Complete and color the picture.

Emu

There are 20 peanuts.
The mother emu eats 10 of them.
The baby emu eats the rest.
Did the mother eat more than the baby? _____

Explain your thinking. _____

_____

Complete and color the picture.

Salt Water Fish

Jasmine is at the zoo.
She wants to buy fish food that costs 25 cents.
She has 3 dimes.
Does she have enough money? _____

Complete and color the picture.

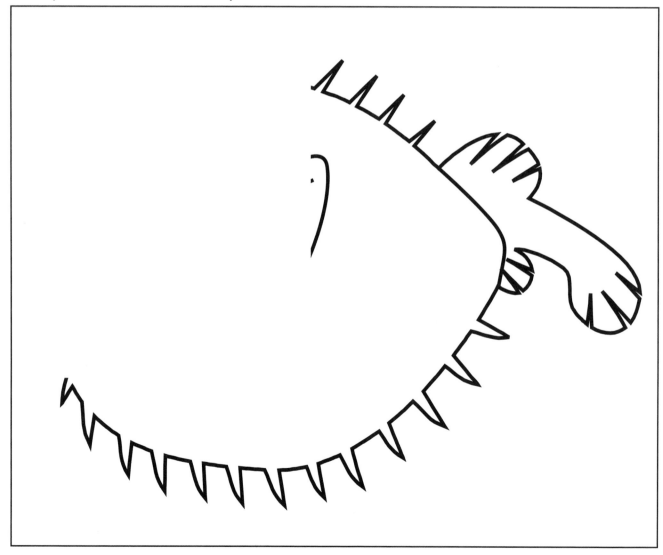

Angel Fish

There are 17 fish swimming in the river.
The bird sees 10 of them and the owl sees 10 of them.

Explain how this can be. _____

_____

_____

Complete and color the picture.

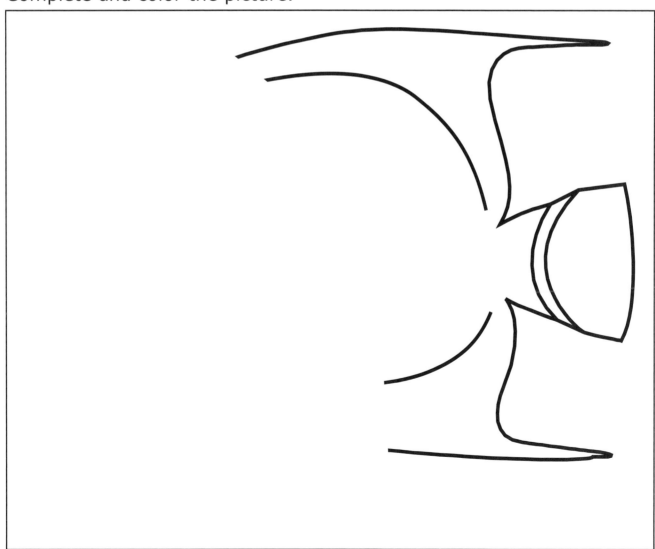

Freshwater Fish

Linda has a fish tank that is 30 inches high.
There is 3 inches of sand at the bottom of the tank.
How many inches is it from the top of the sand to the top of the tank?

_____

Complete and color the picture.

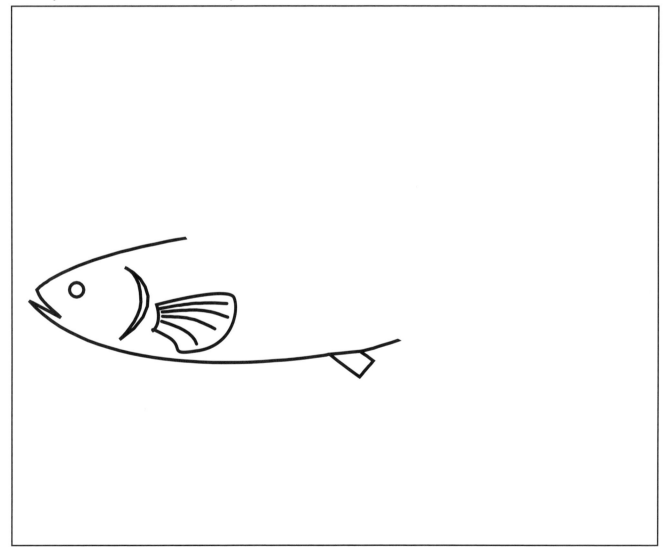

Gold Fish

Brady wants to feed 30 fish.
He has two boxes of fish food.
Each box will feed 10 fish.
Does he have enough food for all the fish? _____

Complete and color the picture.

Flamingo

The flamingo is eight.
How old will he be in one more year? _____

How old will he be in two more years? _____

Complete and color the picture.

Bull Frog

The frog can jump the same distance forward and backward.
One day the frog was on a log.
He jumped forward three hops then backward three hops.

Now where is he? _____

Complete and color the picture.

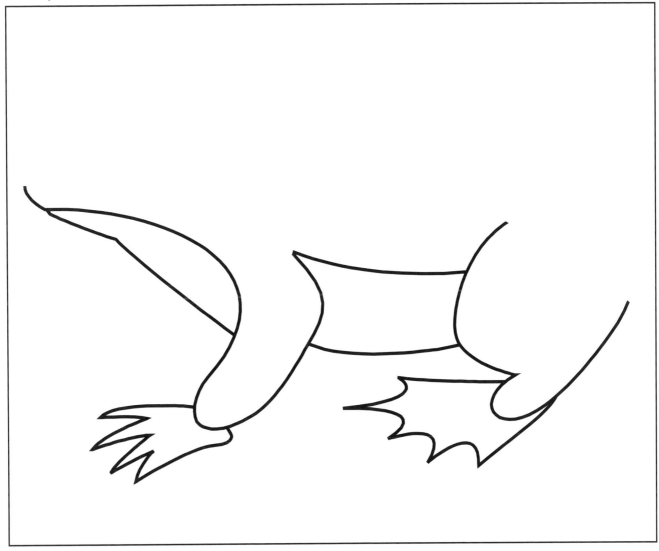

Toad Frog

The frog laid 100 eggs in the pond.
Half of them hatched.
How many frogs hatched? _____

Complete and color the picture.

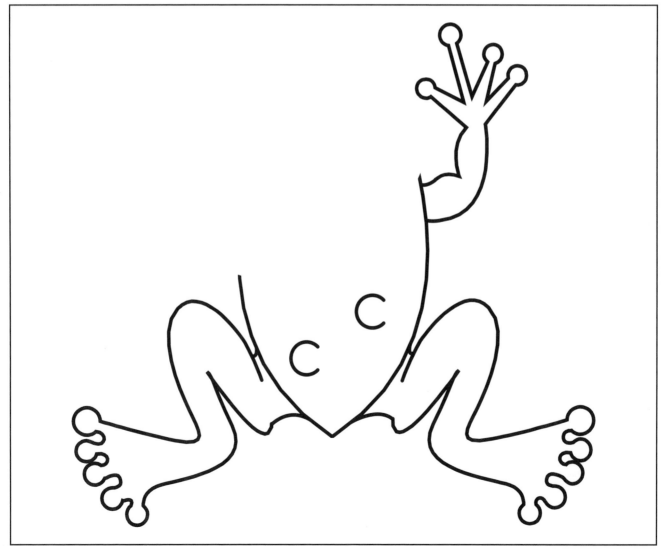

Gazelle

Alice is a gazelle.
She has two brothers and two sisters.
They all live with their mother and father.
How many gazelles are in Alice's family? _____

Complete and color the picture.

Giraffe

The giraffe walked 4 miles.
Then he rested 4 minutes.
Then he walked 4 miles.
How many miles did the giraffe walk? _____

Complete and color the picture.

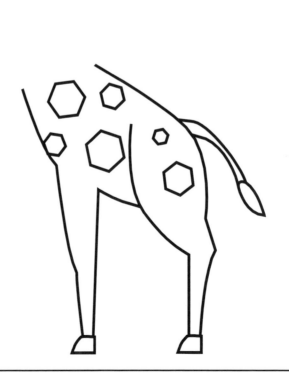

Goat

Paul had to feed the goats.
He woke up at 7:00.
Andy woke up at 8:00.

Who slept the latest? _____

How much later did he sleep? _____

Complete and color the picture.

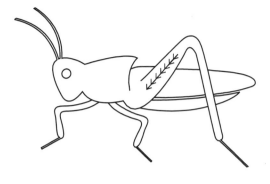

Grasshopper

The brother grasshopper and sister grasshopper are counting their jumps from the house to the pond.
It takes the brother 12 jumps to reach the pond.
It takes the sister 9 jumps to reach the pond.

Whose jumps are longer? _____

Explain your thinking to your teacher.

Complete and color the picture.

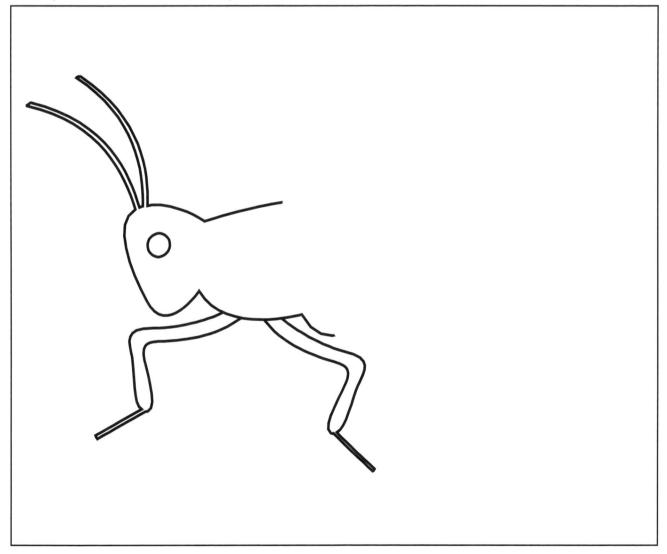

Hedgehog

The hedgehog has a big bunch of berries.
He eats six of them.
Can you tell how many he has left? _____

Explain why or why not. _____

_____

Complete and color the picture.

Gelding

Sara left home and rode her horse four miles to the pond.
Then she rode four miles to her friend's house and then back to the pond.
How many miles is she from her home? _____4_____

Complete and color the picture.

Mare

There are six horses and seven apples.
How many more apples are there than horses? _____/_____
If each horse eats an apple, how many apples will be left over?

_____/_____

Complete and color the picture.

Stallion

The boy had ten apples.
He wanted to feed three horses.
Each horse ate three apples.
How many apples does the boy have left? _____

Complete and color the picture.

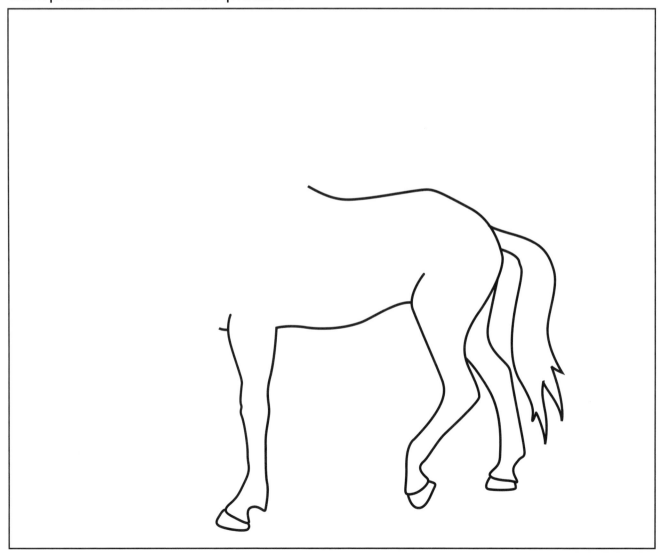

Kangaroo

Kim is first in line at the zoo.
She wants to see the kangaroos.
Carl is behind her.
James is just behind Carl.
What place in line is James? ___3rd___

Complete and color the picture.

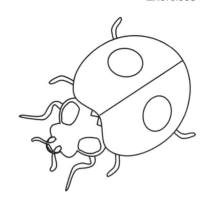

Ladybug

There are three ladybugs in Aaron's yard.
There are six ladybugs in Rosa's yard.
Ryan's yard has two more ladybugs than Aaron's yard.

Whose yard has more ladybugs? _____

Complete and color the picture.

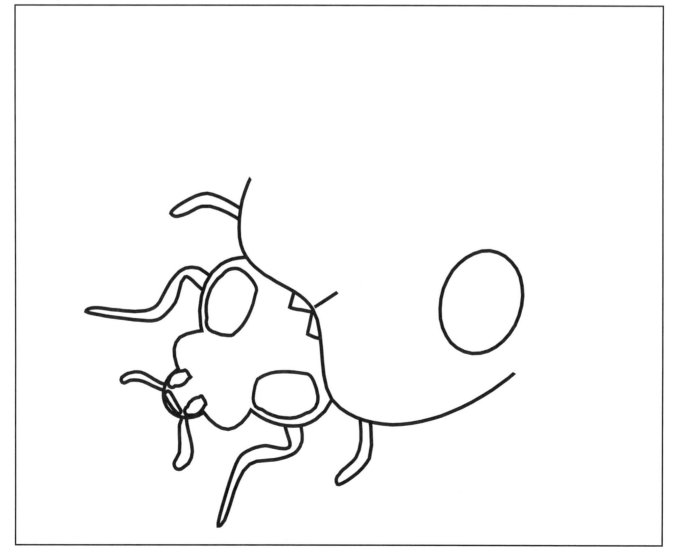

Lemur

There is a bird and two lemurs in the tree.

How many eyes are in the tree? _____

How many tails? _____

How many feet? _____

One lemur climbed down from the tree.

Now how many feet are in the tree? _____

Complete and color the picture.

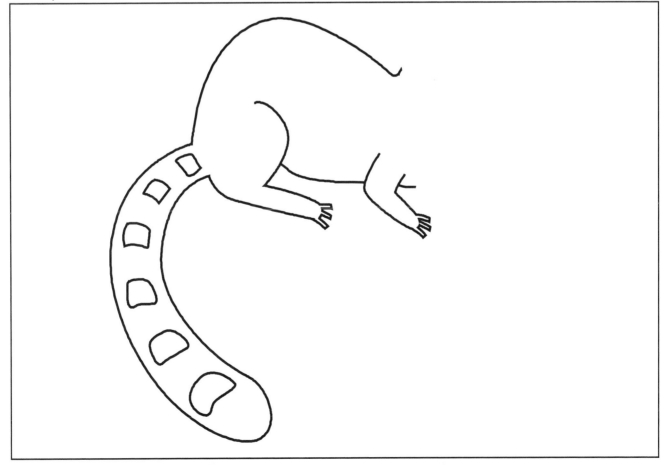

Lion

Kallie wants to see the lions at the zoo.
The tickets cost 25 cents.
Kallie has 2 nickels and 5 pennies.

Does she have enough money? _____

Megan trades her 2 nickels for a dime.

Now does she have enough money? _____

Complete and color the picture.

Tiger

Katrina has two coins.
One is a dime.
At the zoo, food for the tiger costs 15 cents.

Does she have enough money to buy tiger food? _____

Explain why or why not. _____

_____

Complete and color the picture.

Lizard

Shaun needs 57 insects for his pet lizard.
The insects are sold in bags that hold 10 each.
If Shaun buys six bags, will he have enough? _____

How many insects from the last bag will he use? _____

How many extra insects will he have? _____

Complete and color the picture.

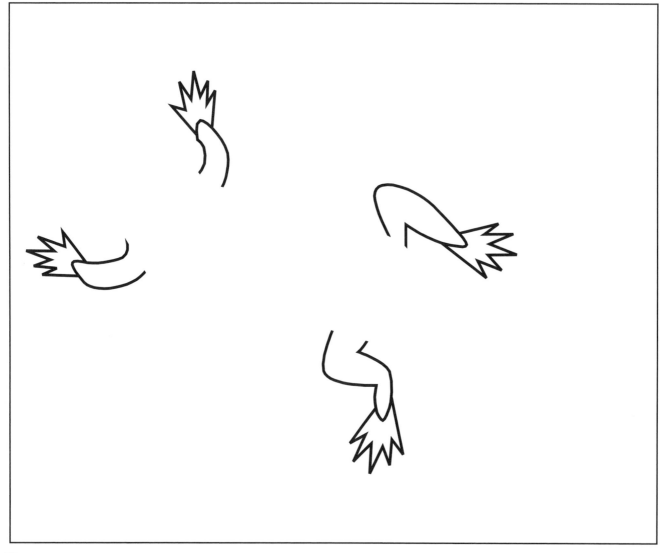

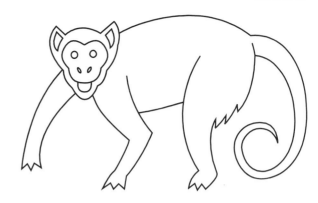

Monkey

The monkey finds a bunch of bananas.
He eats four bananas.
Now he has five left.
Can you tell how many were in the bunch when he found it? _____

Were there less than ten bananas? _____

Complete and color the picture.

Moose

Ethan is at the zoo.
He wants to buy food for the moose.
"The food costs 6 pennies," says Arthur.
"Oh," says Ethan. "I only have 2 nickels."

Can Ethan buy the food? _____

Explain why or why not. _____

_____

Complete and color the picture.

Mouse

Every weekday night the mouse sneaks into the kitchen and looks for cheese.

What did the mouse do on Tuesday night? _____

_____

Complete and color the picture.

Hoot Owl

The owl was at home.
Then he flew 2 miles and found himself at home again.

How could that be? _____

_____

Complete and color the picture.

Barn Owl

The owl wants to fly 14 miles to the river.
He flies 10 miles.
How many more miles must he fly to get to the river? _____

Complete and color the picture.

Pig

The pig has a pen that is square.
How many sides does the pen have? _____

How many corners does the pen have? _____

Complete and color the picture.

Porcupine

The mother porcupine turned six a month ago.

How old will she be next year at this time? _____

The father porcupine turns eight tomorrow.

How old will he be this time next year? _____

Complete and color the picture.

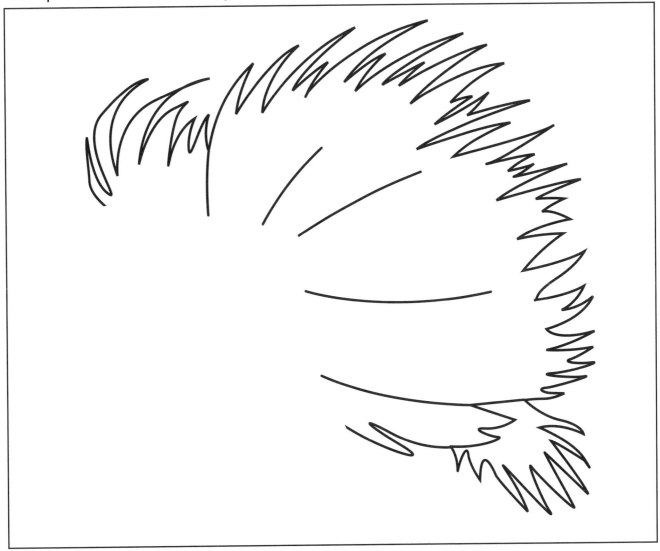

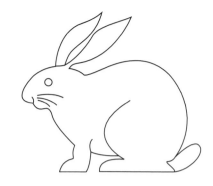

Rabbit

The rabbit had twelve carrots.
He ate all except one of them.
How many does he have left? _____

Complete and color the picture.

Jack Rabbit

The rabbit was eating the vegetables in Mr. Brown's garden.
He ate four rows of carrots.
"That's 4 rows done and 5 more rows to eat," said the rabbit.

How many rows will the rabbit eat if he eats every row? _____

Complete and color the picture.

Raccoon

The raccoon caught eight frogs.
He wants to save two of the frogs.

How many frogs can he eat now? _____

Complete and color the picture.

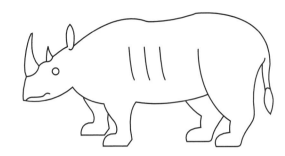

Rhinoceros

The bird felt a raindrop, then another, and another.
The rhinoceros didn't feel any.

How could this be? _____

_____

Complete and color the picture.

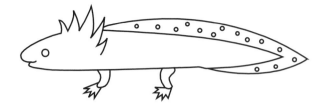

Salamander

Amy has some salamanders.
One salamander is orange.
Can you tell how many salamanders are not orange? _____

If half of Amy's salamanders are orange, how many salamanders does

Amy have? _____

Complete and color the picture.

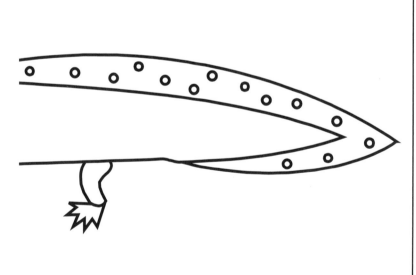

Skunk

The food machine at the zoo has a sign that says, "Please use correct change."
Nadir wants to buy 30 cents worth of skunk food.
He puts in 2 dimes and 2 nickels.

Will that work? _____

Complete and color the picture.

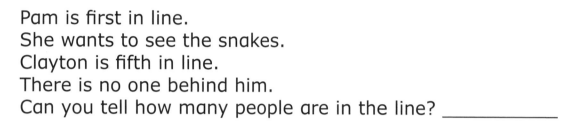

Poisonous Snake

Pam is first in line.
She wants to see the snakes.
Clayton is fifth in line.
There is no one behind him.
Can you tell how many people are in the line? _____

How many? _____

Complete and color the picture.

Squirrel

The squirrel had 30 nuts.
She was very hungry, so she ate all but one.

How many nuts did she have left? _____

Complete and color the picture.

Swan

The swan is 8 years old.
How old was she last year? _____

How old was she two years ago? _____

Complete and color the picture.

Tadpole

Tina found 10 frog eggs.
She put them in a bowl.
Eight eggs hatched.
How many tadpoles did Tina have? _____

Complete and color the picture.

Turkey

Devan has 3 dimes and 2 nickels.
The turkey food at the zoo costs 40 cents.
How much money will Devan have left after he pays for the food?

_____

Complete and color the picture.

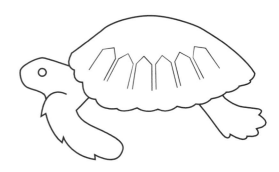

Turtle

The turtle laid 20 eggs.
Half of the eggs hatched.
How many baby turtles are there? _____

Complete and color the picture.

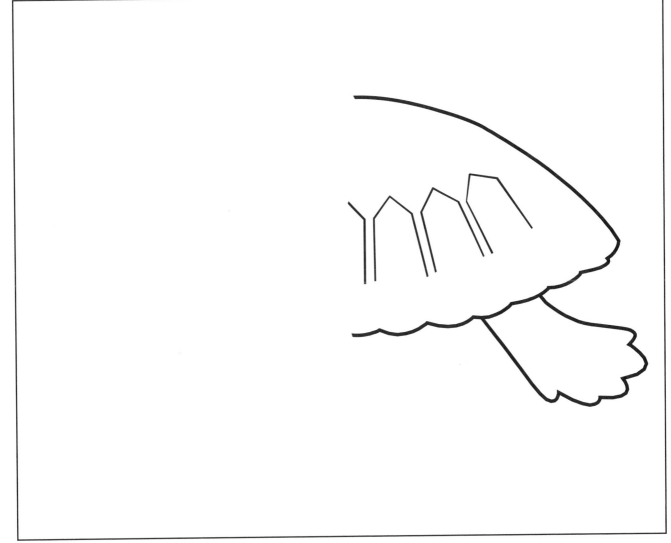

Zebra

The mother zebra and the father zebra decided to walk together to the pond, which is 6 miles away.
The mother zebra walked 3 miles.
The father zebra walked 3 miles.

Are they at the pond yet? _____

How far is it still to the pond? _____

Complete and color the picture.

Non-Poisonous Snake

Stacey and her friends were waiting in line to see the snakes.
Stacey was number six in line.
Thomas was number 10.
How many friends were in between them? _____

Complete and color the picture.

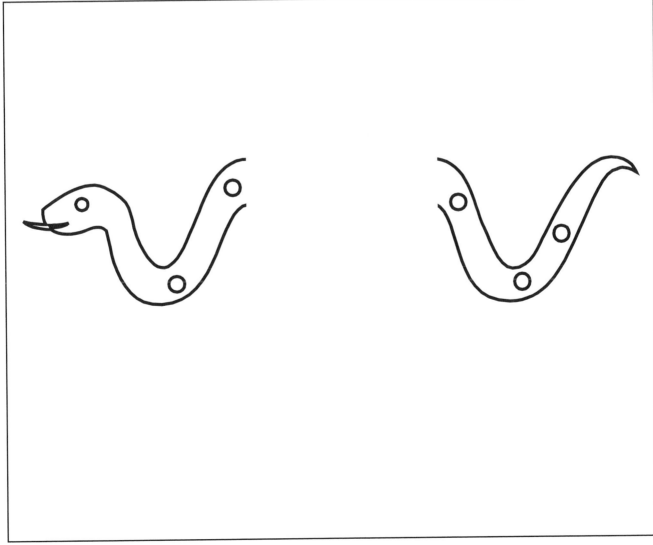

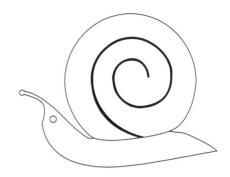

Snail

A snail and a turtle raced to the pond. The turtle finished in half an hour. The snail finished in an hour.
If he didn't get tired, how long would it take the turtle to race to the

pond and back? _____

If he didn't get tired, how long would it take the snail to race to the

pond and back? _____

Complete and color the picture.

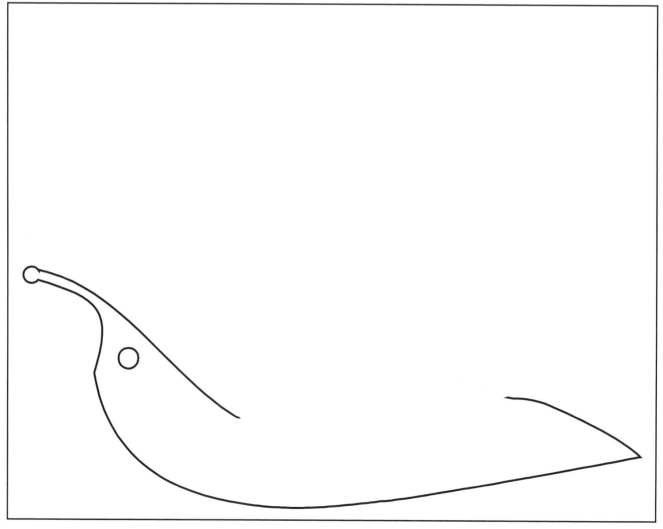

Sheep

There are two sheep.
Each ate half of the food.

How much was left? _____

Complete and color the picture.

Persian Cat

A black cat eats one more treat than a striped cat.
The black cat ate 21 treats.
How many treats did the cats eat altogether? _____

Complete and color the picture.

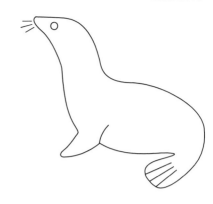

Seal

At the zoo, Tony wants to see the seals.
They perform at nine o'clock.
The minute hand has fallen off Tony's watch.
He says he can still use the watch to tell when it's 9 o'clock.

How can this be? _____

_____

Complete and color the picture.

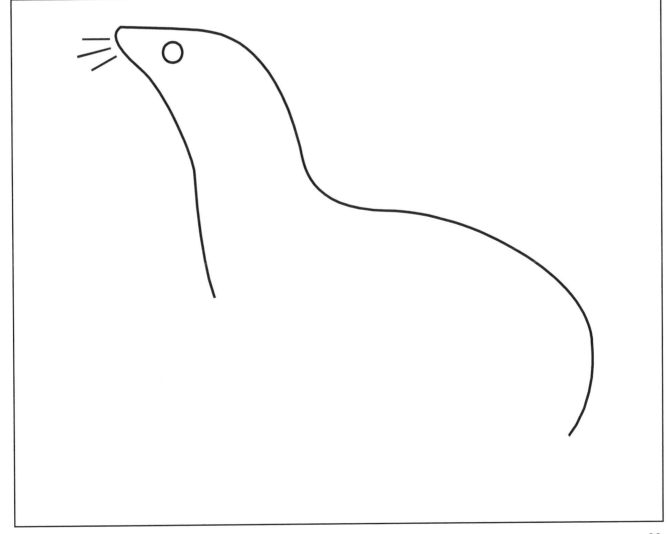

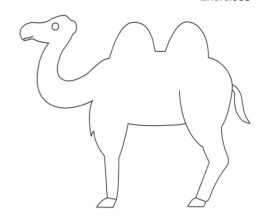

Camel

Camels like hot weather.
The temperature was 100° F.
Was it hot or was it cold? _____
The temperature fell 10° F.
Did it get warmer or colder? _____

What is the new temperature? _____

Complete and color the picture.

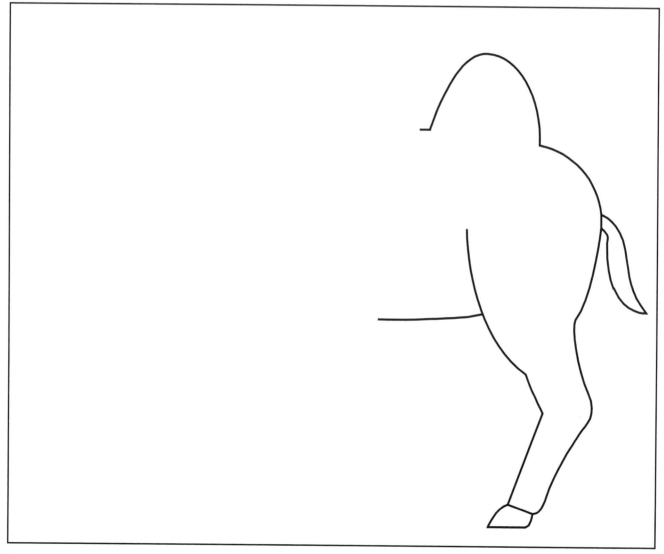

Answers

1. 20
2. 2
3. 8, 9, no
4. yes
5. 7, 6
6. 20
7. 3
8. neither koala
9. 5, 3
10. 9
11. yes
12. no, today is Saturday
13. 8
14. yes, she has at least 15 cents
15. 15 minutes, no, 5 minutes
16. use 1 quarter and 1 nickel
17. 3
18. 16
19. 3
20. yes
21. 1
22. no, yes
23. no, 6
24. 9
25. 7, 7, 1
26. 1 hour
27. 7 miles
28. even, odd
29. no, you don't know how many bones they ate
30. 1
31. 0
32. 7, 13
33. 14
34. 2
35. 2 miles, 10 miles
36. yes, he has either 15 or 20 cents
37. no, they both ate the same
38. yes
39. neither animal sees all of the fish
40. 27 inches
41. no
42. 9, 10
43. at the same place on the log
44. 50
45. 7

46. 8
47. Andy, 1 hour
48. sister, she made fewer jumps
49. no, you don't know how many are in a bunch
50. 4
51. 1, 1
52. 1
53. last (or third)
54. Rosa's
55. 6, 3, 10, 6
56. no, no
57. We do not know. She could have a penny, nickel, or quarter.
58. yes, 7, 3
59. yes, yes
60. yes, 2 nickels equal 10 pennies
61. snuck into the kitchen and looked for cheese
62. he flew 1 mile away from home and 1 mile back
63. 4
64. 4, 4
65. 7, 9
66. 1
67. 9
68. 6
69. the rhinoceros was not in the rain
70. no, 2
71. yes
72. yes, 5
73. 1
74. 7, 6
75. 8
76. 0
77. 10
78. no, 3 miles
79. 3
80. 1 hour, 2 hours
81. 0
82. 41
83. The hour hand will point to the 9.
84. hot, colder, 90°